To Milena, Mariell, and Iwona: baby fish, mummy fish, and granny fish!—A. McQ.
To Immy, my little fish, from Mummy with love—R. H.

And with thanks for their advice, Siblings Afro Hair Design, Slough

First published in the UK in 2016 by
Alanna Books
46 Chalvey Road East,
Slough, Berkshire, SL1 2LR

www.alannabooks.com

ISBN: 978-1-907825-132
Printed and bound in China

(card 1)

Zeki Can Swim!

by Anna McQuinn
Illustrated by Ruth Hearson

ALANNA BOOKS

Zeki loves the water.
He's like a little fish!

Zeki and Daddy are going to swimming class tomorrow.

Zeki puts on his swim nappy and swim trunks in the changing room.

Everything else
goes in the locker.

Everyone says hello.

The babies sit on the edge
of the pool.

Now the class is ready.
The babies slide in.

Then they hold on tight.

Off they go! Kick! Kick! Kick!

They swish and swooosh!

They splish and splooosh!

They sing a
splashy song.

Then Daddy is Daddy Fish
and Zeki is Baby Fish.

Zeki loves that.

Next it's off to the shower.
They use sloshy soap...

and sloppy lotion.

Being a little fish is a lot of work!

After a quick snack, Zeki is fast asleep.